PROSIT

KIPPIS

KAN BEI

DOWN THE HATCH

GOOD LUCK

OKOLE MALUNA

SLÁINTE

SALUD

SALUTE

SKÅL

JAIKIND

CHEERS

VIVAT

ŞEREFE

HERE'S TO YOU

NA ZDOROVIA

TERVIST

KAMPAI

SANTÉ

L'CHAIM

SELAMAT

BANZAI

MABUHAY

BOTTOMS UP

I SVEIKAS

A SUA SAÚDE

ZIVIO

SAWASDI

PROOST

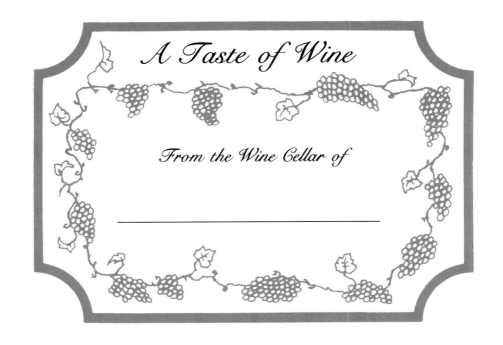

A Taste of Wine

From the Wine Cellar of

_____

KENSINGTON HOUSE PUBLISHING LTD.
New York, U.S.A.

First published in the United States in 1994
by Kensington House Publishing Ltd.
New York, U.S.A.

Printed and bound in Hong Kong
ISBN 1-878518-41-0

Cover: Pierre Auguste Renoir (1841-1919), *The Luncheon of the Boating Party,* 1881
Oil on canvas, 51 x 68 (129.5 x 172.7)
Copyright © 1994, The Phillips Collection, Washington, D.C. (acc. no. 1637)

Wine and Dine

Hors d'oeuvres	*Dry Wines*	Sherry, Moselle, Alsatian
Oysters	*Dry White Wines*	Chablis, Pouilly Fuissé, Graves, Champagne or Moselle
Soup	*Medium Dry Wines*	Madeira or Sherry
Fish	*Dry White Wines*	Burgundy, Graves, Champagne, Hock or Moselle
Game & Meat	*Dry Wines*	Claret, Burgundy or Champagne
Poultry	*Dry Wines*	White Burgundy, Hock or Dry Light Red Wine
Sweets	*Sweet White Wines*	Sauternes, Barsac or Champagne
Cheese	*Rich Red Wines*	Port, Brown Sherry or Red Burgundy
Dessert	*Rich Red Wines*	Port, Brown Sherry or Madeira
Coffee	*Brandy or Liqueurs*	

Note: Champagnes and many of the Dry Hocks and Rosé Wines may be drunk throughout the meal.

A helpful guide to selecting a wine can be found by reading the label. If the label bears the name of a particular chateau or vineyard, then it is proud of its birthplace and more than probably first class. Next in line comes the label bearing just the village name, followed by the one that only mentions a district, and finally the label that simply states Bordeaux Red or Burgundy White, etc. Exceptions, however, are champagnes which usually have their own special housemark and German wines where the entire pedigree generally appears on the label.

Wine Name _____

Vintage: _____

Bottled by: _____

Obtained from: _____

Cost: _____

Type: _____

Appearance: _____

Nose: _____

Taste: _____

Balance: _____

Occasion served: _____

_____

_____

_____

Comments:

_____

_____

Place
Label Here

Wine Name _____

Vintage: _____

Bottled by: _____

Obtained from: _____

Cost: _____

Type: _____

Appearance: _____

Nose: _____

Taste: _____

Balance: _____

Occasion served: _____

_____

_____

Comments:

_____

_____

Place
Label Here

Wine Name _____

Vintage: _____

Bottled by: _____

Obtained from: _____

Cost: _____

Type: _____

Appearance: _____

Nose: _____

Taste: _____

Balance: _____

Occasion served: _____

_____

_____

_____

Comments:

_____

_____

Place
Label Here

Wine Name _____

Vintage: _____

Bottled by: _____

Obtained from: _____

Cost: _____

Type: _____

Appearance: _____

Nose: _____

Taste: _____

Balance: _____

Occasion served: _____

_____

_____

_____

Comments:

_____

_____

Place
Label Here

Wine Name _____

Vintage: _____

Bottled by: _____

Obtained from: _____

Cost: _____

Type: _____

Appearance: _____

Nose: _____

Taste: _____

Balance: _____

Occasion served: _____

_____

_____

_____

Comments:

_____

_____

Place
Label Here

Wine Name _____

Vintage: _____

Bottled by: _____

Obtained from: _____

Cost: _____

Type: _____

Appearance: _____

Nose: _____

Taste: _____

Balance: _____

Occasion served: _____

_____

_____

_____

Comments:

_____

_____

Place
Label Here

Wine Name _____

Vintage: _____

Bottled by: _____

Obtained from: _____

Cost: _____

Type: _____

Appearance: _____

Nose: _____

Taste: _____

Balance: _____

Occasion served: _____

_____

_____

_____

Comments:

_____

_____

Place
Label Here

Wine Name _____

Vintage: _____

Bottled by: _____

Obtained from: _____

Cost: _____

Type: _____

Appearance: _____

Nose: _____

Taste: _____

Balance: _____

Occasion served: _____

_____

_____

Comments:

_____

_____

Place
Label Here

Wine Name _____

Vintage: _____

Bottled by: _____

Obtained from: _____

Cost: _____

Type: _____

Appearance: _____

Nose: _____

Taste: _____

Balance: _____

Occasion served: _____

_____

_____

_____

Comments:

_____

_____

Place
Label Here

Wine Name _____

Vintage: _____

Bottled by: _____

Obtained from: _____

Cost: _____

Type: _____

Appearance: _____

Nose: _____

Taste: _____

Balance: _____

Occasion served: _____

_____

_____

_____

Comments:

_____

_____

Place
Label Here

Wine Name _____

Vintage: _____

Bottled by: _____

Obtained from: _____

Cost: _____

Type: _____

Appearance: _____

Nose: _____

Taste: _____

Balance: _____

Occasion served: _____

_____

_____

_____

Comments:

_____

_____

Place
Label Here

Wine Name _____

Vintage: _____

Bottled by: _____

Obtained from: _____

Cost: _____

Type: _____

Appearance: _____

Nose: _____

Taste: _____

Balance: _____

Occasion served: _____

_____

_____

_____

Comments:

_____

_____

Place
Label Here

Wine Name _____

Vintage: _____

Bottled by: _____

Obtained from: _____

Cost: _____

Type: _____

Appearance: _____

Nose: _____

Taste: _____

Balance: _____

Occasion served: _____

_____

_____

_____

Comments:

_____

_____

Place
Label Here

Wine Name _____

Vintage: _____

Bottled by: _____

Obtained from: _____

Cost: _____

Type: _____

Appearance: _____

Nose: _____

Taste: _____

Balance: _____

Occasion served: _____

_____

_____

_____

Comments:

_____

_____

Place
Label Here

Wine Name _____

Vintage: _____

Bottled by: _____

Obtained from: _____

Cost: _____

Type: _____

Appearance: _____

Nose: _____

Taste: _____

Balance: _____

Occasion served: _____

_____

_____

Comments:

_____

_____

Place
Label Here

Wine Name _____

Vintage: _____

Bottled by: _____

Obtained from: _____

Cost: _____

Type: _____

Appearance: _____

Nose: _____

Taste: _____

Balance: _____

Occasion served: _____

_____

_____

Comments:

_____

_____

Place
Label Here

Wine Name _____

Vintage: _____

Bottled by: _____

Obtained from: _____

Cost: _____

Type: _____

Appearance: _____

Nose: _____

Taste: _____

Balance: _____

Occasion served: _____

_____

_____

_____

Comments:

_____

_____

Place
Label Here

Wine Name _____

Vintage: _____

Bottled by: _____

Obtained from: _____

Cost: _____

Type: _____

Appearance: _____

Nose: _____

Taste: _____

Balance: _____

Occasion served: _____

_____

_____

_____

Comments:

_____

_____

Place
Label Here

Wine Name _____

Vintage: _____

Bottled by: _____

Obtained from: _____

Cost: _____

Type: _____

Appearance: _____

Nose: _____

Taste: _____

Balance: _____

Occasion served: _____

_____

_____

_____

Comments:

_____

_____

Place
Label Here

Wine Name _____

Vintage: _____

Bottled by: _____

Obtained from: _____

Cost: _____

Type: _____

Appearance: _____

Nose: _____

Taste: _____

Balance: _____

Occasion served: _____

_____

_____

_____

Comments:

_____

_____

Place
Label Here

Wine Name _____

Vintage: _____

Bottled by: _____

Obtained from: _____

Cost: _____

Type: _____

Appearance: _____

Nose: _____

Taste: _____

Balance: _____

Occasion served: _____

_____

_____

_____

Comments:

Place
Label Here

Wine Name _____

Vintage: _____

Bottled by: _____

Obtained from: _____

Cost: _____

Type: _____

Appearance: _____

Nose: _____

Taste: _____

Balance: _____

Occasion served: _____

_____

_____

_____

Comments:

_____

_____

Place
Label Here

Personal Wine List

Name	Type	Year	No. of Bottles

Personal Wine List

Name	Type	Year	No. of Bottles

Personal Wine List

Name	Type	Year	No. of Bottles

Personal Wine List

Name	Type	Year	No. of Bottles

Personal Wine List

Name	Type	Year	No. of Bottles

Personal Wine List

Name	Type	Year	No. of Bottles

Personal Wine List

Name	Type	Year	No. of Bottles

Personal Wine List

Name	Type	Year	No. of Bottles

Personal Wine List

Name	Type	Year	No. of Bottles

Personal Wine List

Name	Type	Year	No. of Bottles

Personal Wine List

Name	Type	Year	No. of Bottles

Personal Wine List

Name	Type	Year	No. of Bottles

Personal Wine List

Name	Type	Year	No. of Bottles

Personal Wine List

Name	Type	Year	No. of Bottles

Personal Wine List

Name	Type	Year	No. of Bottles

Personal Wine List

Name	Type	Year	No. of Bottles

Personal Wine List

Name	Type	Year	No. of Bottles

PROSIT

KIPPIS

KAN BEI

DOWN THE HATCH

GOOD LUCK

OKOLE MALUNA

SLÁINTE

SALUD

SALUTE

SKÅL

JAIKIND

CHEERS

ŞEREFE

VIVAT

HERE'S TO YOU

NA ZDOROVIA

TERVIST

KAMPAI

SANTÉ

L'CHAIM

SELAMAT

BANZAI

MABUHAY

I SVEIKAS

BOTTOMS UP

A SUA SAÚDE

ZIVIO

SAWASDI

PROOST